Tales from the Touchline
Pep Guardiola
by Harry Coninx

Published by Raven Books
An imprint of Ransom Publishing Ltd.
Unit 7, Brocklands Farm, West Meon, Hampshire GU32 1JN, UK
www.ransom.co.uk

ISBN   978 180047 241 9
First published in 2021

TALES FROM THE TOUCHLINE

PEP GUARDIOLA

HARRY CONINX

RAVEN

For Dad, my first manager and the only man
who thinks he knows more than Pep

CONTENTS

I

ANFIELD

February 2021, Anfield, Liverpool, England
Liverpool v Man City

"When was the last time we won at Anfield, then?" Pep asked, glancing over at his assistant Rodolfo Borrell, who was sitting next to him in the dressing room.

"Us?" Rodolfo replied. "Never. The club? 2003."

His reply hung in the air. Pep had swept every team aside whilst he'd been in charge at Man City, but Liverpool at Anfield had always been a problem. Jürgen

Klopp and his team had always found a way to get a win against them.

"No crowd today, though," Rodolfo added. "COVID means it's still an empty stadium. That's got to be big."

Pep nodded. The crowd at Anfield was one of the loudest and most intimidating in the whole of Europe. When Liverpool played in front of this crowd, their players always went up another gear.

"Let's go over the team," Pep said, grabbing the team sheet from Rodolfo. It was almost time for the players to go out, and he wanted to give them some final words.

"So," he began, looking at the Liverpool team, "are we sure it's Fabinho and Henderson at centre-back? He won't go Kabak or Phillips?"

"It's confirmed," Juan Manuel Lillo added.

"So that's their weak point," Pep said. "You take Fabinho out of that midfield and they lose that … "

He stopped talking, gesturing with his hands.

"And Henderson," Rodolfo added.

"Yeah, you take out those two and they lose that energy," Pep continued.

"So we press high, put the pressure on those

centre-backs," Rodolfo said. "Make them try and play out from the back."

"I want us to split into a 4-4-2," Pep said. "When the centre-backs move out wide, Foden and Sterling push up high and onto them. We win the ball back quickly."

Moments later, Pep was giving his pre-match talk to the players. "I know how we feel about Anfield," he told them, making sure that he had their full attention. "I know Liverpool are the champions. I know they have Salah, Mané, Firmino. But we have Sterling, Gündoğan, Mahrez. We have John Stones, Dias, Ederson. We have big names as well. *We're* the team who have won thirteen consecutive games. *We're* the team who've won two titles in a row. There's no fans today, there's no atmosphere. It's just 22 guys on the pitch."

The players nodded. It was on Pep now to convince them they could win.

"High pressure from the start. I want us to dictate the tempo. I want us to be the ones running the game."

Even without the crowd, the atmosphere inside the stadium was tense. City might be top of the league, seven points clear of Liverpool, but there was still a lot to play for.

"We win tonight, it might be your biggest achievement," Rodolfo chuckled. "It sends a message to the rest of the league."

"Tonight?" Pep replied. "I think when we win the title – that'll be the biggest moment."

He strolled out with his team, walking behind the players and glancing around the empty stadium. Anfield was normally a wall of sound where he could barely hear himself think, but today the stadium was silent.

The empty stadiums had actually been a great benefit to Pep. Now he could shout to his players and they could all hear him and follow his instructions.

As he came out onto the touchline, he was approached by Liverpool manager Jürgen Klopp, the man who had beaten him more than any other. A huge smile was on his face.

"Pep," he said warmly. "Welcome back to Anfield. I hope you're going to go easy on us tonight."

"I would never," Pep replied. "I'm sure you've got a trick or two up your sleeve to make it hard for us."

A few moments later, the game began. Pep leaned back in his chair, taking in the first ten minutes from his seat on the bench. The game was tight and cagey. City had the majority of the possession, but they were struggling to make it count.

Every so often, he rose and barked an order to one of his players. "Kyle, quicker!" he yelled at Walker, as he dallied on the ball.

Eventually City got their first chance. Raheem Sterling skipped his way into the box, before being taken out by Fabinho.

Pep's instinctive competitive edge kicked in – as if he was still one of the players on the pitch.

"Penalty!" he bellowed, turning towards the referee.

As İlkay Gündoğan stepped up to take the penalty, Pep whispered, "Come on, İlkay." His body was tense, but he kept the calm look on his face. He was the pillar of this team – they were looking to him for reassurance.

City had had an awful time with penalties recently, especially against Liverpool. Gündoğan stepped up, but he blazed the ball high and wide over the bar.

"Oh come on!" Pep groaned, circling around his dugout in frustration. "Why does this always happen to *us*?" he said, turning back to Rodolfo.

"The goal is coming," Rodolfo replied. "There's going to be chances for us."

At half-time, Pep was frustrated. They'd dominated the ball and missed a penalty. They needed to be ahead.

"Guys, we've had 45 minutes to get the game, to feel our way in," he said. "Now we step it up. Higher energy. We don't give them time to start getting the ball."

"Alisson is looking weak," Rodolfo added. "He's normally one of their best on the ball, but several of his passes have gone astray today. When he gets it, make him play it, make him try and look for the pass. There's a chance it will go wrong."

Minutes into the second half, City took the lead. Sterling drove into the box and laid the ball back to Foden, whose shot was blocked by Alisson. But the ball came straight back out to Gündoğan, who smashed it in.

"They can't handle Phil's running," Pep said calmly. He knew that one goal wouldn't be enough to win this game.

The goal didn't signal a City onslaught, but Pep hadn't been expecting that to happen. Liverpool weren't the champions for nothing.

Moments later, Salah was brought down in the box, before converting the resulting penalty.

"So, they can score their penalties," Pep moaned.

The next five or six minutes were all Liverpool. They were starting to get a foothold in the game, and City's normally relentless possession had been replaced by desperate chasing.

Pep was experienced enough to know that it was time for a change, time to freshen things up.

"Gabi!" he shouted, looking at Gabriel Jesus. Jesus was City's only fit striker, although Pep had chosen to start with Phil Foden in that role.

"If we move Phil out to the right, you go down the middle," he said to Jesus as he warmed him up. "Phil is causing them all kinds of issues out there, so you'll have plenty of space. I want a lot of energy, a lot of running. Don't let them settle."

It only took a minute for Jesus to make an impact. He put pressure on Alisson, who made a sloppy pass. The ball went to Foden, then it was with Gündoğan and in the back of the net. Now City had the lead.

"We need a third!" Pep shouted, calling over his

captain Raheem Sterling. "Let them know," he continued. "Get a third and then we relax. We're not going to defend a 2-1 lead."

He needn't have said anything. A second Alisson mistake allowed Bernardo Silva to feed Sterling, who made it 3-1.

Then, with ten minutes left, Phil Foden scored a spectacular solo goal to make it four.

City hadn't just *beaten* Liverpool – they'd thrashed them.

Pep had outclassed the last team that he'd struggled to beat, the team that had won the league last year and who'd knocked City out of the Champions League a couple of years before that. And Klopp too, the manager who'd caused him more problems than any other.

"You know what?" Pep said, turning to Rodolfo. "You might be right. This *might* be my biggest achievement."

"Ten points clear of Liverpool," Rodolfo added. "Still in every competition. Let's wait 'til we win the quadruple, shall we?"

Pep smiled. He was one of the greatest managers in the world. With him at the helm, it all felt very possible.

2

A BARCELONA PLAYER

July 1984, La Masía Academy, Barcelona, Spain

"Josep! Come on!"

Pep stopped juggling the ball that he'd been keeping in the air. His parents rarely used his full name – it usually meant that they were frustrated with him.

"Why are you messing around with a ball?" his dad, Valenti, asked, shaking his head. "We're literally on our way to a football trial. It's like you're addicted."

"I'm just getting some last-minute practice in!" Pep protested, as he followed his dad out to their car.

The truth was, he was very nervous. Today was the biggest day of his life so far. At just 13 years old, he had the opportunity to trial for the club he'd supported his whole life – Barcelona. The club where Johan Cruyff, Johan Neeskens and Diego Maradona had all made their names.

So many thoughts were running through his mind. Would he be good enough to make it into the team? Would he be turned away immediately? Would that be his football career done, before it had even begun?

That's why he'd gone into the garden and started juggling the ball. It relaxed him, made him feel more at ease. When it was just him and the ball, he didn't have to worry about whether he'd get into the Barcelona youth team.

"So, do you know where you want to play today?" his dad asked him, jolting Pep back to reality.

"What do you mean?"

"Your position," his dad chuckled. "Have you got one in mind?"

"Wherever they'll take me, I guess," Pep shrugged.

His dad laughed again. "You can't tell them that, Pep."

"Why not?" It was the truth. He honestly didn't mind where he played, as long as he got into the team.

"This is Barcelona, Pep," his dad replied. "One of the biggest clubs in the world. You can't just turn up and play *anywhere*. You have to show that you know what you're doing. Otherwise they won't respect you."

Pep nodded. If he wasn't already feeling enough pressure, his dad had just added a whole lot more.

Pep usually played around the front three, on the right of the midfield. It was where he was the most dangerous. So that was what he'd tell the coaches.

Every year, around a thousand of the most talented kids in the country turned up to trial for Barcelona. But only 200 would be selected to join the academy. And today was the day that they would be whittled down. Today was the day that 800 would leave broken-hearted. Pep was determined not to be one of them.

They arrived at La Masía and were soon divided up and put into sets of mini-games on the large training ground.

"I play on the right," Pep said, as the coach began sorting out the teams. "Right midfield." He said it assertively, following his dad's advice.

The coach laughed. "We know what all of you are good at," he said. "We know what you like and where you play. But this is Barcelona. This is about testing you against the best. Testing what you're uncomfortable with."

He chucked Pep a bib and directed him over to the other side of the pitch. "You'll be playing on the left."

The first game was tougher than anything Pep had ever experienced. He barely got a touch of the ball for the first ten minutes. Everyone was desperate to impress and the pace was ferocious.

But then he started to drift into the middle, getting some more touches on the ball. He was starting to dictate play, spraying passes across the pitch and even dribbling past players. He was no Maradona, but he had the ability to move past players, and he was keen to show that off. He wanted them to see the range of his skills. He wanted them to know that he could do anything, play anywhere, just as long as it was at Barcelona.

When the games eventually came to an end, Pep was exhausted. He'd forgotten all his nervousness whilst he'd been playing, but now that the games were over, the nerves came flooding back.

There were no more opportunities now. There was nothing he could do to prove to the coaches that he belonged here. His parents were back with him now and his dad came and stood next to him. The coaches were gathered in a huddle, whispering and conferring.

Nobody could affect their decisions now. He could only watch and pray. Either he was a Barcelona player – or he wasn't.

After an agonising wait, the coaches began reading out names – the names of the lucky players who had made it into the academy …

" … Josep Guardiola!"

The name rang out across the training ground. It was so unusual for him to hear his full name read out like that, he almost didn't recognise it.

But this time it didn't mean he was in trouble. This time it meant he was a Barcelona player.

3
IN THE PIVOT

December 1989, La Masía Academy, Barcelona, Spain

"Can't I just move inside and get a touch on the ball?" Pep asked the coaches, before quickly being told – again – that he had to stick close to the right touchline.

When he'd first joined Barcelona, they'd told him that he wasn't going to have a set position, but now that had changed.

There were strict sets of rules for Barcelona players,

from the first team right down to the academy. All the players had set positions. You could play from within that position, but everyone had a specific role on the pitch, with strict instructions on what to do during each stage of play.

Pep had been moved out to the right-hand side of midfield, the position he'd asked for when he'd first started at the academy. But he often found himself isolated on the side of the pitch, unable to get involved or get touches on the ball.

The only good thing about being on the right-hand side was that he got the best view of the game. It was a manager's view of the game.

He could see where his team-mates were when they had the ball, and he could see where they needed to be. He could tell too which opposition players were out of position – and he often ended up dictating play and dishing out advice.

He may have been struggling to impact games directly, but he was able to get his friends and team-mates touches on the ball and help them get the ball forward.

"You should be a manager, Pep," Jordi Roura would often tell him. "You could probably retire now and go on to be a manager."

"I can't be a manager now, I haven't even started as a player yet!" Pep laughed.

The latest training match was more important than usual. Johan Cruyff, the legendary player and new Barcelona manager, had come down to cast his eye over the latest set of youth players. This was a real opportunity for them to show him what they could do – and perhaps even win a place in the first-team squad.

Pep started once more on the right-hand side and he didn't expect too much of himself. After ten minutes he still hadn't got a touch on the ball and was resigning himself to a useless game.

But then it struck him. He was wasting his time stuck out on the right. How many times would he get to play in front of Johan Cruyff? This man was his idol, the player he'd looked up to as a kid. He was desperate to impress him.

Just as he'd done on his trial day, Pep started to drift inside, getting more and more touches on the ball. He ignored the barked orders of the coach and played his way into the middle of the pitch.

At half-time the Academy team manager, Charly Rexach, came over to him. "Pep," he said with a grin.

Pep glanced over, expecting a telling-off, although the smile told a different story.

"Change of plans for the second half," he said. "You're going to play in the pivot. Johan's orders."

"Pivot?" Pep asked, a little surprised.

The pivot, or defensive midfield position, was one that was rarely used by any team in Spain. It was the connection between defence and midfield and was a hard position to do well. It would be key for the team in progressing the ball forward, but it also required discipline to stay in front of the defence.

"Yeah. He thinks it will be good for you," Rexach said. "And you'll be good at it."

Pep nodded. It made sense that the position would suit him. He would get to see the whole game from the base of midfield, he'd get a lot of touches on the ball and he'd be able to use his range of passing. It just sounded right.

The second half was the best game of football Pep had

ever played. He had more touches of the ball than he'd had in the last five games combined. He was at the heart of the action, just where he'd been desperate to be.

Pep was the beating heart of the team, connecting the midfield, the defence, the forwards. He could direct people where to go, he could pick out passes, tackle opposition forwards, even dribble forward into space. Every aspect of his game was perfect for the role.

Thinking about it afterwards, Pep had no idea how Johan had spotted it. He'd never have thought of it himself. It was a bold decision to look at the position that someone had played their entire life – and then tell them that they would be better at something else.

It was a skill he'd be keen to learn himself.

Pep had only been half-joking when he'd dismissed Jordi's comments that he was ready to be a manager. He was already feeling that a career on the touchline was waiting for him.

But then, just a year later, he joined the Barcelona first team. Johan had decided to bring him in.

4
TOTAL FOOTBALL

May 1992, Wembley Stadium, London, England
European Cup Final, Barcelona v Sampdoria

"We want to play something called *Total* Football," Cruyff said, putting the emphasis on the "total".

Pep nodded. He was vaguely familiar with the concept, although he didn't know a lot about it. Not that he was going to let Cruyff know that he wasn't sure what his manager was talking about.

"I want everyone to be able to play in every position,"

Cruyff continued. "If you have players that are excellent in just one position, you won't have a strong eleven – you'll just have eleven strong ones."

He looked down at Pep, checking that he was taking it all in. Pep almost felt as if he should be writing everything down.

"If you move forward with the ball, into space, José Bakero should be able to move into *your* position and cover. If José moves in like that, then Ferrer should be able to step forward and take *his* position. So everyone can play everywhere."

It made sense, but this kind of total, free-flowing football wasn't just a free-for-all. Players had to know what to do when team-mates moved into other roles. Five or six times in each training session, Cruyff would stop play and step in to show players what he needed them to do.

His tactical instructions were having clear results on the pitch. Barcelona raced to the very top of the league and were flying in both the domestic cup and the European Cup.

Pep was at the heart of it, and every week he was learning something new from Cruyff.

"Everyone talks about running, about moving around a lot, but I don't agree," Cruyff said after one session. "I say, *don't* run so much. You need to play football using your brain more. You have to arrive at the right place at the right moment – not too early, not too late."

This was something that suited Pep. He'd never been the quickest of players, or someone who could physically dominate a game. But he was smart – he knew where he needed to be and when to get there. It meant that whenever he got the ball, he had space all around him.

As the season went on and the pressure on Cruyff to deliver a trophy became greater, there were fewer and fewer chats between him and Guardiola. Cruyff seemed to become more and more focused on getting results.

Although, as he'd always told Pep, "Quality and entertainment without results is pointless. But – results without quality? That's boring."

Barcelona won the league on the final day, with a 2-0 win over Athletic Bilbao in a style that was anything but boring.

It then came down to the final of the European Cup, a trophy Barcelona had never won in their history. And now Pep was part of the team that had an opportunity to do just that – to become a part of history.

They were meeting Sampdoria in the final and everybody knew it would be a tough game.

"How are you feeling, Pep?" captain Andoni Zubizarreta asked him in the dressing room, before the game.

Pep was one of the younger players in the squad – a squad that was full of superstars. But he was also one of the most important. If he didn't do his job well, then the team couldn't function.

"I'm alright," Pep said, guardedly.

He didn't want the captain to know how nervous he was. He didn't want him to know that he was worried about Sampdoria's front two of Roberto Mancini and Gianluca Vialli. He didn't want him to know that he was worried about the atmosphere inside Wembley.

He just wanted him to think he was alright.

"I'm sure the boss will have a few words," Zubizarreta said, patting Pep on the back.

Pep agreed. He'd been sure that Cruyff would spring some kind of tactical shock for the final, something that

Sampdoria wouldn't be expecting. But instead he'd stuck with their usual formation. Nevertheless, Pep was expecting some detailed instructions before the game began.

In the dressing room, Cruyff stood up, looking over the squad, and a smile appeared on his face.

"We deserve to be here, guys. We deserve to win. Now go out there and enjoy yourselves."

That was all he said. There were no tactical instructions, no big speeches. But, for some reason, that was all they needed. He had faith in the players that he'd picked, the players that had been playing for him all season. There was nothing they needed to change.

The game was played at a ferocious pace, tougher than anything Pep had experienced before. With so much at stake, all the players were feeling the pressure, making mistakes they wouldn't normally make. Even Pep's passes weren't as crisp as usual.

That was the one thing that even Cruyff couldn't account for – pressure, the human ability to make mistakes.

Vialli missed chances for Sampdoria, and Salinas and

Laudrup both went close for Barcelona. But after 90 minutes there was no separating the sides, and the game lurched into extra time.

There was an added factor now – fatigue. Pep could barely put one foot in front of the other. His body was telling him that he needed to go off, to sit down, to stop. But his head was desperate to stay on, to be part of history.

With barely ten minutes left, Barcelona won a free kick just outside the box. They'd practised routines like this and they knew exactly what to do. The ball stopped in front of Ronald Koeman, who ran onto it and blasted it towards the goal. There was no stopping it as it flew into the far corner of the goal.

A moment later, Pep was off. He knew the game was in the bag now and his race was done. He could watch the rest of the match from the bench. He didn't move again until the final whistle was blown and he was able to collect his medal and get his hands on the giant trophy.

Barcelona had won their first ever European Cup – and Pep had not just been part of it, he'd been integral to it.

He couldn't wait to do it again.

5
CALM UNDER PRESSURE

March 1997, Nou Camp, Barcelona
Barcelona v Atlético Madrid

As Pep walked down the tunnel after the first half, he heard Barcelona's head coach, José Mourinho, muttering to himself.

"We're screwed," he heard him say.

As the players sat in the dressing room, all eyes were on their manager, Bobby Robson. They had some idea of the intense pressure he was under. Surely, with all that was going on, he wouldn't be able to give them the kinds of words they needed to hear right now.

But Robson didn't look at all like a man under pressure. Instead, he was calm and deliberate.

"We're Barcelona, lads," he said, looking at each of them. "That means something. It means something to me – and I know it means something to all of you. But at the moment, you're not playing like it."

The success of Barcelona's "Dream Team" under Cruyff had gone well beyond their first European Cup trophy. They'd won a number of league titles and trophies, and they'd even reached a second European Cup final – where they'd been roundly trounced by Fabio Capello's Milan side.

Milan played very differently to Barcelona, and in that game they'd managed to stifle the possession style that usually worked so well for Barca. It had been the first time that Cruyff had seemed human to some of the players.

Pep was still a disciple of Cruyff's total football, but he'd also seen that there was another way. He thought that Cruyff's reluctance to change his mind or change his tactics might have cost them their second European trophy.

"How can you blame the boss, though?" Pep would argue. "Without him we would never even have got that far."

"Come on, Pep," Ronald Koeman countered. "The man is a genius, that's for sure, but people have grown wise to it. They know exactly what we're going to do."

As the seasons had gone on, Barcelona's results had worsened. Teams had learnt how to deal with Cruyff's way of playing.

Pep didn't have the answers. Cruyff would always be his hero – he would always be the man who'd given him his chance and created the Barcelona dream team.

But there were no complaints when Cruyff was sacked.

He was replaced by Bobby Robson, who didn't really share the same beliefs as Cruyff. Robson brought with him some big names – Brazilian striker Ronaldo, Laurent Blanc and Luis Enrique, among others.

He built a strong squad.

Robson focused on man management, leaving the tactics mainly to his assistant and translator, José Mourinho. They spent a lot of time focusing on practising defensive transitions and defending the goal.

It was wildly different to Cruyff, but Pep couldn't help noticing the similarities.

"If you don't concede, you can't lose," José would often remark.

"Johan used to say, if you keep the ball you can't lose," Pep replied.

Either way, Barcelona started getting decent results. But the fans still weren't happy with how the team was playing, and the board was desperate for a trophy to ease the tension.

Then it all came to a head one night in the Copa del Rey. Barcelona had drawn the first leg 2-2 with Atlético Madrid, getting two vital away goals. But at home in the second leg, after a dismal display in the first half, they came in trailing by three goals.

As he came off the pitch at half-time, Pep could see the fans waving white handkerchiefs in the air. It was a sign of their disapproval. It was a sign that they hated the manager and wanted him gone.

Now, in the face of all that, Robson had the job of getting his players back into the game.

"We're Barcelona, lads," Robson told them again. "It

doesn't matter what happens in this second half. It doesn't matter what happens to me after this game. You need to do this for yourself. Show some pride for the shirt you're wearing. Fight until the end, until the game is done and dusted and we're back in here again.

"Because, until you're back in here again, this game is still up for grabs."

His words were calm, but they were delivered with passion. He was asking the players to show some fight, to show that they deserved to wear the shirt.

Barcelona came back out for the second half with renewed vigour. The game was up and down, but Barcelona fought back to beat Atlético Madrid 5-4.

It was a famous win, one of the greatest nights of Pep's career, even up there with the 1992 European Cup win. But Pep didn't think about the game. He thought about the words that Robson had spoken in the dressing room.

In that moment, the weight of the world had been on Robson's shoulders, and he hadn't shown it. He'd spoken to the team without once raising his voice.

If Pep hadn't been certain he wanted to be a manager, he was now. He wanted to be like Robson.

6
INTO MANAGEMENT

April 2008, Mini Estadi Stadium, Barcelona, Spain
Barcelona B team training ground

"Johan is a big fan of yours, Pep, and keeps going on about you," Laporta told him. "He wants you here as part of our team. What do you think?"

Pep was flattered at being approached in this way by Barcelona's president, Joan Laporta. Although Johan Cruyff was no longer manager at Barcelona, Laporta still relied heavily on him for advice.

"Possibly upper management," Laporta continued. "Technical Director? Sporting Director? You can pretty much pick your role."

The arrival of two incredibly gifted young midfielders, Andrés Iniesta and Xavi, had pretty much signalled the end of Pep's time in the Barcelona first team. He'd already sensed that his career was winding to an end, and after brief spells in Italy and the Middle East, he had eventually retired.

It was then that he'd been able to consider his choices. He'd always been certain that he was going to go into management and, with his coaching badges done, it was simply a choice of where he would go.

Pep had always hoped that he would return to Barcelona one day, but he hadn't anticipated being given the opportunity quite so soon.

Laporta's offer was a huge honour, and it was an even greater honour that his hero, Johan Cruyff, had recommended him. The opportunity to work with Cruyff again wasn't one that he could really turn down.

But Cruyff had spent most of the last few years stuck on the side-lines, out of the action. He wasn't at the centre of things, and Pep didn't want to start his coaching career sitting in the boardroom, even if it was alongside Cruyff.

"Is there anything a bit more hands-on?" Pep asked Laporta, interrupting him as he ran through the benefits of each role.

"Sorry?" Laporta asked, clearly not used to being interrupted.

"Something with a bit more coaching," Pep replied. "Like on Rijkaard's coaching staff? Or the B team?" Frank Rijkaard was the current Barca manager, so it was a bold move for Pep to be asking to join his team.

"I mean … I guess the B team is available," Laporta said, "but you don't want to go down there, do you? They just got relegated. We're working hard to change it, but it's a mess right now, Pep. That's why we want you in the boardroom. Someone we can trust."

Pep was well aware of the issues within the Barcelona boardroom. He knew all about the difficult politics that were involved in running the club. It was the same politics that had led to the exit of Johan Cruyff as manager, twelve years earlier. He wasn't interested in being involved in something like that. He just wanted to focus on the football.

"I'll take the B team," he said, firmly. "Let me see if I can turn them around."

"OK," Laporta sighed. "The job's yours."

With his position as Barcelona B team coach secured, Pep immediately went about recruiting his staff. He turned to his trusted friends Tito Vilanova, Domènec Torrent and Carles Planchart. They were all men who he knew shared his footballing philosophy and believed in the same Cruyffian style of play that Pep had grown up on.

The next job was to start looking at the squad. The team had been relegated to the fourth level of Spanish football, and there were a number of players who were low on confidence.

"So who are the players we want? Who are our key guys?" Pep asked.

Carles and Domènec had been studying the team whilst Pep had been sorting out everything with the board. Now he was keen to hear their thoughts.

"That kid Busquets is very good," Carles said,

immediately pointing out the tall defensive midfielder. "In the pivot he is going to be a star."

"I want to see more of Pedro and Jeffrén further forward," Domènec added. "A lot of pace, trickery, flair. You need a bit of that."

"Pedro? Really?" Pep asked. "The other coaches here weren't so sure about him."

"I disagree. I think he's a top player," Domènec continued. "Trust me, Pep, you'll need him going forward."

"What were you thinking tactically?" Carles asked. Pep sensed they had their own ideas, but they were keen to let him lead the way. He was the manager, after all.

Pep was excited finally to get to try out his own tactics. For so many years he'd been subject to a range of other people's ideas and tactics. He'd been able to give his opinions, but he'd never been able to develop his own tactics from scratch. This was his opportunity.

"4-3-3," Pep replied. "Three creative midfielders, we retain possession of the ball at all times. I want quick, short passes and when we get it forward we go quickly – we can use the wingers you wanted."

"I don't know, Pep … " Carles replied.

"What are your thoughts, then?" Pep asked him.

"We're down here in the Tercera División, we're going to be on some awful pitches. The ball will bounce and bobble. It won't be easy to do crisp, short passes."

"It might be easier to do something using longer balls, get the ball wide and whip in crosses," Domènec added.

"No. That's the style I want to play," Pep insisted. "We've got the players to do it."

He was reminded of Johan Cruyff, the man he admired the most. Cruyff had stuck by his principles through everything, refusing to change his style of play or his team, even in the toughest of circumstances.

That was how Pep wanted to be. And if he could make that style of play work on these kinds of pitches, down in the Tercera División, then it would work anywhere.

This was just the start. They were going to sweep to promotion playing beautiful, creative football.

7

BARCELONA ARE BACK

May 2009, Santiago Bernabéu Stadium, Madrid, Spain
Real Madrid v Barcelona

"Congratulations, Pep, on being the new Barcelona first-team manager." Joan Laporta grinned as he shook Pep's hand warmly.

The past few months had been a complete whirlwind. Pep had guided the Barcelona B team to a play-off win and promotion, but then Frank Rijkaard, manager of the first team, had been sacked.

The favourite to replace him had been José Mourinho, but Johan Cruyff, who was still on the Barcelona board, had intervened, getting Pep appointed instead.

Pep brought Tito Vilanova to join him in the first-team, and their first job was to go through their squad. For the first time, Pep had an opportunity to actually make some transfers, sell some players and bring new players in. This was the exciting part of being a manager.

"So," Pep began, "what's our situation?"

There was a moment of silence from the coaching team. It was common knowledge that the situation at Barcelona was far from ideal. If they were in a good place, Pep would never have been hired.

"I think there's definitely some room for changes … " Vilanova said cautiously.

"We keep Xavi, Iniesta," Pep mused, getting to the point. "We build the team around them. And Messi of course."

"I hate to say it, but … " Domènec began.

" … Ronaldinho can go." Pep finished his sentence, saying what they were all thinking.

Former Ballon d'Or Winner Ronaldinho had been Barcelona's number 10 and star player for several seasons, but over the last year or two he'd shown signs of decline.

"I think we need big decisions," Pep continued. "There's players in this team whose opinions are greater than their ability. There's no room for that. We need young, hungry players – players who have something to prove and will fight for this shirt."

Over the next month, he began to whittle down his squad. Experienced players, including Deco, Ronaldinho, Lillian Thuram and Gianluca Zambrotta, were all allowed to leave.

Then Pep had to deal with another side of football management, a side that Johan Cruyff had detested – the press.

"How are you going to get by without Ronaldinho?"

"Who's going to replace Zambrotta in defence?"

"Do you think you've made a mistake taking the job?"

And those were just the questions that were asked to his face. The headlines in the papers were even harsher, accusing him of being out of his depth. He was being written off before the season had even begun.

But Pep had a few tricks up his sleeve, with a few key replacements lined up. Busquets and Pedro were promoted from the youth team, Gerard Piqué rejoined as a centre-back from Man Utd and Dani Alves was signed for huge money as a new right-back.

But the biggest change was what Pep was planning to do with the players already at his disposal.

"So we put Messi down the middle," Pep said, looking at his assembled coaches.

"What?" Domènec replied. "The middle? He's a winger! Where are you going to put Henry and Eto'o?"

"Out wide."

"What are you thinking exactly?" Vilanova asked. He knew Pep well enough to appreciate that this wasn't just a random tactic. There had been real thought behind this.

"Messi is our best passer, our best dribbler, our best striker of the ball," Pep continued. "We don't want him stuck out wide. We need him at the centre of the action."

"He'll lose every physical battle," Domènec replied.

"Not if he doesn't get involved in them," Pep said. "If he drops into the middle, away from the centre-backs, he doesn't worry about that. That creates panic for the opposition – they don't know whether to follow him or leave him."

"Henry and Eto'o push inside … " Vilanova said, considering the tactic. There was a small smile on his face, and Pep could tell he was already a fan.

Over the next year, the tactic worked pretty spectacularly. Barcelona swept all aside, firing their way to the top of La Liga and into the latter stages of the Copa del Rey and the Champions League.

But, despite their good form, they just couldn't shake the reigning champions, Real Madrid. Their next game was away to their famous rivals, in the cavernous Santiago Bernabéu Stadium. Real were four points behind Barca and a win would keep them in the hunt for the title.

As usual, Pep met with his team before the game.

"So they've gone for 4-4-2, then," Pep said, glancing over the Madrid team. "Ramos and Robben. That's the weakness. And Heinze on the other side."

"Let's move Messi out wide," Vilanova added. "At least for the start. Let him run at their full-backs."

"Agreed." Pep said, continuing to look at the team.

He didn't need to say much to his coaches. By now, it had all become second nature to them. The only thing that concerned him was the pressure. They'd beaten everyone with nothing riding on it. But now the title was on the line, could they handle it?

"We don't need to change anything," he said. "It doesn't matter that it's Real Madrid. It doesn't matter where we are. We do what we've done for the whole of the season – and we win."

Even so, the opening goal came from Real Madrid. Gonzalo Higuaín powered home a header, after Ramos got into space on the right-hand side.

Just a few seconds after the goal, Pep made his decision. He turned to Vilanova on the touchline.

"Messi down the centre," he said. He didn't even wait for the reply before he was on the edge of his technical area, barking the orders onto the pitch.

"Leo!" he called. "In the middle, swap with Eto'o!"

Only a few minutes later, it paid off. Messi picked the ball up in the middle of the pitch, drawing Cannavaro out of the Madrid defence. The space was opened up for

Thierry Henry, who sprinted through the middle. Messi's pass was inch-perfect, as was Henry's finish.

Two minutes later, Barca were 2-1 up. Henry was fouled by Cannavaro out wide and Puyol hammered home a header from the free kick.

Pep didn't celebrate the goal. They were only 20 minutes into the game and he needed to keep his focus.

"Cannavaro," Pep said, instead turning to Vilanova on the touchline. "He's the weakness. If we draw him out, we get space. There are more goals here."

Just before half-time, Barca doubled their advantage. Xavi dispossessed Diarra in midfield and played a pass into Messi, who fired past Casillas.

At half-time they were 3-1 up and cruising away from their closest title rivals and the biggest rivals in their history. A win here would effectively seal the title.

"Normally, guys, in this position we would think the game is won," he told them in the dressing room. The players nodded, expecting him to say that they were going to shut up shop. It made sense now to hold onto the win, see the game out and win the title.

"So I'll tell you what I want you to do," he continued.

"I want more goals, because there are more of them out there for us. Leo, the centre-backs cannot stay with you. Thierry, you have the pace to beat them."

Pep continued, laying out his tactical instructions. He just didn't know how to shut up shop, to change his style and hold on for the win. He remembered Cruyff's words – results without entertainment are boring.

"We may concede two or three, guys, but we will score five or six," he said. "I promise you, we will be the team who scored six at the Bernabéu. That will be us."

As the players looked at him, he could sense that they trusted him completely. They were all on his side and already in full support of him. He knew they were going to win. He knew the title would be theirs.

At full-time, they walked back in 6-2 winners. They hadn't just beaten Real Madrid, they had annihilated them. They'd sent out a clear message to the rest of Spain and the rest of Europe.

Barcelona were back.

8
THE TREBLE IN YEAR ONE

May 2009, Stadio Olimpico, Rome, Italy
Champions League final, Barcelona v Man United

"How are you feeling then, son?" Sir Alex Ferguson's gruff Scottish accent boomed in Pep's ears as he shook hands with the opposition manager. This was a man who had won it all with Manchester United, including a famous treble back in 1999 – the very thing that Pep was going for tonight.

"Your first European Cup final tonight, right?" Ferguson continued, his hand still pressed into Pep's.

"As a manager, yeah," Pep replied.

"It's different as a coach," Ferguson continued. "You can't influence the game like you used to. Not everyone can handle it." There was a smile on his face, but Pep felt as if he was sizing him up, working out what kind of manager he was. He'd been warned about this side of management – the mind games.

"I think I'll be fine," Pep said, matching Ferguson's smile and keeping the handshake going.

"Good luck out there," Ferguson laughed, becoming the first one to break the handshake and turn away.

"What was that all about?" Tito Vilanova asked, as Pep turned and returned to his own bench.

"Just trying to get under my skin," said Pep, brushing it off. "What do we think of their team?" he continued, ignoring Tito's questioning eyebrow.

"Park, Rooney, Giggs, Anderson … " Tito said, reading off the list of names.

"I know what the team is," Pep sighed. "But what do we think?"

"It's good for us," Tito replied. "He's worried about us going forward."

"Then they won't be able to take advantage of our defensive issues," Pep replied. He was right. Barcelona had a number of injury problems in defence and had put out a makeshift back four, featuring Yaya Touré at centre-back.

"They're not the most mobile midfield, especially without Scholes," Pep continued. "If we move the ball quickly, I think we can dominate this."

"What about Ronaldo?" Vilanova asked.

"Don't let him get it," Pep said confidently, settling back in his seat. "He can't do anything if we don't let him get the ball."

The match had been billed as Messi v Ronaldo, but there was so much more at stake. Barcelona were going for the treble and Man United were going for a second Champions League in a row. Winning would be the making of Pep as a manager and would cement his status in Barcelona folklore.

Pep knew that the key to the game was going to be in the middle of the pitch, where Barca's strengths lay. Messi in the false nine position, dropping deep and dragging the United centre-backs out of position.

Within ten minutes, Barcelona got their first goal. Messi laid the ball off to Iniesta, who drove deep into the United half. He passed the ball to Samuel Eto'o, who skipped into the box and flicked it past the keeper.

"Come on!" Pep roared, instinctively pumping his fist.

Glancing at the United bench, Pep could see that Ferguson was secretly steaming, but outwardly he looked calm. Pep lowered his fist and focused on controlling his emotions. There were 80 minutes left to play – he didn't want his players seeing him getting carried away.

"Xavi!" he shouted, gesturing for his midfielder to come over to the side of the pitch. "We keep doing what we're doing, OK? Passing, moving, nothing changes, OK? We don't go for two, we don't try and hold on, OK?"

Xavi nodded. He was Pep's general on the pitch, his representative in the team. If Pep wanted a message passed on to the rest of the team, he went through Xavi.

Barcelona continued to hold onto the ball, and for an hour they passed their way around the Man Utd midfield. To some it was boring, but to Pep it was magical. It was everything he had ever dreamed of. It was perfect.

But it was still only 1-0, and now United had thrown on their big guns in Carlos Tevez and Dimitar Berbatov.

Then Xavi got the ball on the right-hand side. The game had opened up, with United pushing for an equaliser, and Pep had spotted the space for Messi in the box. He'd seen the pass, but he didn't know if his midfielder had.

He needn't have worried. Xavi too had seen the pass and floated the ball into the box. Messi rose high above the defence and met the ball with his head. It rose high into the air, before landing in the back of the net.

Once more, Pep let out a roar and instinctively pumped his fist. This time he didn't try to hide his reactions.

The next 20 minutes were all Barcelona. It was a 20 minutes in which Pep could take in the magnitude of what he'd achieved in his first year at Barcelona. The treble.

Pretty much nobody had ever done that, let alone in their first year managing a club. And he'd done it playing football *his* way – Cruyff's way.

"This is just the start," he said, turning to Tito as the final whistle went. "Enjoy tonight. But, this is just the start."

9

OLD FRIENDS, FIERCE RIVALS

November 2010, Nou Camp, Barcelona, Spain
Barcelona v Real Madrid

"So it's José v Pep once again," Mourinho smiled, putting an arm around Pep's shoulder.

Both managers remembered that night back in April, when José's Inter Milan had knocked Barcelona out of the Champions League. Pep's team had done everything right that night, dominating possession and winning the game 1-0. But Inter had gone through, winning 3-2 on aggregate.

Pep remembered Mourinho sprinting around the Nou Camp pitch, pointing a finger in the air. He remembered the day Inter won their own treble. And he remembered the day that Mourinho was announced as the new manager of Real Madrid.

Pep's old friend and colleague at Barcelona had now become one of his fiercest rivals – as well as manager of Barcelona's most hated team.

And today they were playing against each other.

"It's Real Madrid v Barcelona," Pep corrected him.

"Of course, of course," José chuckled. "It's Messi v Ronaldo, Ramos v Puyol, Xavi v Alonso. It's about *them*, not us. We're just two men at the side, shouting words."

"Something like that," Pep shrugged.

He didn't want to get involved in a long conversation with José. He knew how those went, and he knew he usually didn't come out on top. Pep wanted his football to do the talking, he wanted his team of eleven players to show how good they were. *That's* how you came out on top – not with words.

Real Madrid made a quick start but Barcelona quickly began to dominate possession, spraying passes around in their typical style. Early on it became clear what Madrid's tactics were. Every so often Alonso or Khedira would foul one of Barcelona's players, stopping their passing getting into a rhythm.

And every time a Barcelona player went down, Mourinho would be on his feet with an arm in the air.

"Never a foul! Dive!" he'd roar, turning and gesticulating in front of the fourth official.

After the third or fourth time, Pep felt compelled to intervene.

"You know that's a foul," he said, marching to the edge of his technical area. "He took him clean out!"

"You're trying to get my players booked!" José responded in turn. "Busquets is rolling around like he's been shot!"

"We're just trying to play football," Pep snarled.

Eventually the fourth official got in between them, ordering both managers back to their seats. Pep turned away in disgust, seeing a small smirk appear on José's face. He'd got exactly what he wanted.

"We have to beat him now," Pep snapped to Tito. "We can't let him win."

He shouldn't have worried. A moment later a ball in the box deflected into the path of Xavi and he deftly lifted it over Casillas, into the goal.

Ten minutes after that, Pedro tapped in a cross and Barcelona were leading 2-0.

The noise in the stadium went up another notch, but Pep didn't react to either goal. He wasn't ready to celebrate just yet. And he didn't want a narrow, scrappy win. He wanted a demolition, a thrashing – he wanted a message that said that this beautiful, tiki-taka football of his was the best way to play football.

"That smirk's gone now," Tito chuckled, nodding over to the Real Madrid bench, where José sat stony-faced.

The two goals changed the Real Madrid game plan. Now they weren't just playing football – it had escalated to all-out war. First Ronaldo shoved Pep when the ball didn't come his way. Pep laughed it off, but his team were less than impressed and for a minute all 22 players were pushing and shoving in front of the dugout.

A minute later, Messi went down after catching an arm from Carvalho. Once more, the teams began to push and shove, with several players picking up bookings.

"Calm it down!" Pep shouted, trying to make himself heard over the noise in the stadium. The last thing he needed was a player getting sent off. They couldn't allow Madrid a route back into the game.

He reiterated the point to his players at half-time.

"We are playing so well, guys, so well," he said. "But we focus on the football, we keep doing what we're doing. We play our passes. If they kick you, go down, don't react. If they push you and poke you, you don't react."

"You can't let them just get away with it, boss!" Dani Alves protested.

"Maybe they will, maybe they won't," Pep said. "But you have to let the referee do his job. Give him a decision to make on *them*, not on you."

He didn't need to tell them what to do going forward, or how to create chances and score goals. They already knew how to do all that.

David Villa scored two in quick succession early in the second half. Barcelona were now leading Real Madrid 4-0.

The game was now becoming the thrashing that Pep had hoped for. Now it was turning into an exhibition match. Barcelona were able to hold on to the ball, moving it too quickly for Madrid. Every pass was being met with a huge cheer from Nou Camp crowd.

But there was still a bigger cheer to come. Jeffrén added a fifth in the dying minutes of the game, to put another level of gloss on the victory.

If Pep thought that being 5-0 up would take away from José and Madrid's tactics, he was sorely mistaken. Even in the last seconds there was a horrible foul on Messi, and then Ramos lashed out at Puyol.

There was nothing that Pep could do as his players raced in, joining the brawl, grabbing and pushing at the opposition.

Pep glanced over at Mourinho, who once more had a wry smile on his face. Barcelona may have just thrashed them 5-0, but Pep knew that Real Madrid were going to be their biggest challenge this season.

No doubt, it was going to be his toughest year to date.

10
THEATRICS AND TACTICS

April 2011, Santiago Bernabéu Stadium, Madrid, Spain
Real Madrid v Barcelona

It seemed like a lifetime ago that Barcelona had battered Real Madrid 5-0. Pep had dominated the El Clásicos during his time as Barcelona manager and for a long time it looked as if Barcelona were on course for another treble.

But that had all changed. Tonight, Barcelona were playing their third game against Real Madrid in the last two weeks. They had drawn the first one in the league and then lost in the Copa del Rey final. That final in particular had been a tough pill for Pep to swallow. He'd felt his team were the better side and he was frustrated with some of the refereeing decisions that had gone against them. His frustration had obviously been picked up by José Mourinho and, once again, the Madrid manager had voiced his criticisms in a press conference.

"Don't rise to it," director of football and old friend Andoni Zubizarreta told him at the training ground, before the next game.

"I won't," Pep reassured him. His focus was totally on the next meeting between Real Madrid and Barcelona – the Champions League semi-final.

But Pep was feeling the pressure. Mourinho had publicly called him and the Barcelona team out, and Pep had his players to think of. This time, he couldn't stay silent.

"José has spoken directly to me, so I will do the same," he said to a packed room of journalists. "Tomorrow at 20.45 we take to the pitch. Off the pitch, he has already won. I won't play that game. We will see him on the pitch tomorrow."

Short, simple – and to the point.

"You did the right thing, boss," Xavi told him, as soon as he arrived back at the training ground. A few of the other senior players agreed.

"You can't just let it go," Puyol added. "Now they know we're not just going to sit quietly and take it."

Pep had pushed back and suddenly it felt like a release of the pressure that had been building all season. The constant digs and insults from José, the constant criticisms of the referee and Barcelona's "diving".

The game was played with the same atmosphere as the previous three. It was bad-tempered and ugly, with constant fouls. Real Madrid made it clear early on that they were going to try to hold out for a 0-0 draw.

Pep prowled the touchline, anxiously rubbing his hands together. Barcelona had a lot of the ball, but it was all in their own half and there was no pace to it. All their play was going through the middle, just where Real Madrid wanted them.

"We're playing into their hands," he said, turning to Tito.

"We just have to be patient," Tito replied. "They can't do this for 90 minutes."

Pep wasn't so sure. They probably couldn't do this for 90 minutes, but he knew that José probably had another trick up his sleeve. He would have something planned.

At half-time, after another fracas involving all 22 players and several technical staff, Pep got his players together.

"Look, guys," he said. "Let's forget everything in the press, forget everything they do. We are not playing well enough. I don't care if they kick you, you keep doing what we've done all season. Because right now, we're not doing that."

"Pedro," he said, calling his winger over. "You swap with Villa and go on the right. And you stay wide, stretch them a bit more. It's too easy for them right now."

Pep knew that the only way to get to Real Madrid now was if he made them work. The game was all happening in the middle of the pitch. At the moment it was all going José's way.

"He's brought on Adebayor," Tito said.

"I knew it," Pep muttered.

José was now bringing on a physical striker, to pose a different kind of threat to the Barcelona back four. The

Madrid setup was now completely different, with Ronaldo moved out wide to take on Puyol, who was playing as a makeshift left-back.

Then, in the second half, the game changed completely in the space of a couple of minutes. A rash challenge from Pepe saw him red-carded, and moments later Mourinho joined him, sent to the stands with a red card of his own.

Pep remained calm throughout. He didn't need his players seeing him worked up or anxious – and anyway, inwardly he now felt a sense of relief. The absence of Mourinho, who he'd been able to see pacing and shouting out of the corner of his eye, had lifted a weight from his shoulders. Now he could focus on the football.

Pedro had failed to follow Pep's instructions and, with Madrid down to ten men, Barca needed to make the pitch as big as possible. It was time for a change. He summoned Ibrahim Afellay to replace Pedro, giving him the same instructions.

"Stay wide," he said. "Let the ball come to you – you'll have the space."

Within five minutes, the change paid off. Afellay got

the ball on the right and drove into the box, spotting Messi's run. There was nobody else you'd want in that position, and Messi only needed one touch to put the ball in the net.

Pep could take some credit for making Barca's first goal, but he had no influence on their second. That was all Messi. Picking the ball up inside the Madrid half, Messi drove towards the box, passing several of the defenders before flicking it over Casillas.

Barcelona had sealed a brilliant 2-0 win. They'd ignored Madrid and José's theatrics and mind games and come out on top.

"That should be enough," Tito said, as they entered the tunnel.

"Enough for what?" Pep asked.

"Enough to get us into the final."

Pep could only laugh. He'd been so involved with the drama and intensity of the game he'd completely forgotten it was a Champions League semi-final.

Barca now had a real opportunity to get their second European trophy under Pep. He was determined to bring it home.

II
TIRED

April 2012, Nou Camp, Barcelona, Spain
Champions League semi-final, Barcelona v Chelsea

"Another Champions League semi," Pep sighed.

Yet again, he was sitting next to Tito Vilanova in the dressing room, working out how to try to get to the final of the Champions League. Barcelona had won it last year and had followed that up with victories in the Super Cups and in the World Club Cup.

But that was where the glory had stopped. Real

Madrid were a different side this season and had already gone a long way clear in La Liga. The title was all but theirs. Barca may have been in the Champions League semis, but they had lost the first leg 1-0 to Chelsea in a deeply frustrating tie.

"I don't think we need to change anything from the first leg," Tito said, flipping through a little folder containing his analysis of the first-leg tie. "We were all over them – it could have been three or four-nil to us."

"But it wasn't," Pep replied. "Now they're going to sit deep and be compact. If we move Alexis further forward, he can be a difference-maker."

Alexis Sánchez was one of Barca's new signings, alongside Cesc Fàbregas. Today, the pair of them would be key. Alexis was a hard worker and very quick, whilst Cesc had become a ruthless finisher under Pep.

"Their centre-backs," Pep continued, "Terry and Cahill. They're not the quickest, so if we move around them, make them work, they won't like it."

"We did that last week," Tito replied.

"It was all in front of them, it was easy," Pep said, frowning. "We need to be more direct."

Pep was concerned about this coming game. He was tired and was struggling to work out exactly what to do to break down this Chelsea defence. He just had to trust in his players, have faith that they'd do what he'd trained them to do.

As usual, Pep spoke to the players before the game. "We've got to be quicker today, guys. Every pass needs to be quicker, OK?"

He clapped his hands together. "Sharper, quicker, OK, guys? Everything in the first leg, but faster."

He continued talking, but it was almost as if he was going through the motions. He was saying the same things he'd been saying all season, and he wasn't sure the players were buying it. Perhaps they sensed his doubt.

Was there a feeling tonight that it was all going to go wrong, that Chelsea were going to get the result?

For half an hour it was all Barcelona. They had all the possession, but the chances just weren't coming. It was all wild shots from distance, whilst Chelsea were having clearer-cut chances.

"We need to work it into the box," Pep groaned. "These long shots are pointless."

But then they got a breakthrough. Isaac Cuenca squared – for Busquets to tap home. A moment later, John Terry saw red when he kneed the back of Alexis Sánchez. Now Barca had a goal and a man advantage. But they still needed a second goal.

They got their second five minutes later, when Messi threaded a ball into the path of Iniesta, who slid it past Čech. Now Barca were on the verge of going through.

That was until Ramires struck, with a brilliant chip that gave Chelsea the crucial away goal.

At half-time, Pep was lost for words. Barcelona had an extra man and they had been playing brilliant football. But, somehow, they were still on the verge of being knocked out.

"One goal, guys," Pep told his players. "One goal is all we need. That's all we need to win."

His words didn't seem to have much conviction behind them. Everything they did was being dealt with by Chelsea.

Pep wondered once again whether they needed a Plan B. Their Plan A just wasn't getting them anywhere.

In the second half, Messi fired a penalty against the

crossbar, which seemed to say it all. Chelsea seemed to have everything going their way tonight. And when Fernando Torres raced through in the final minutes, Pep didn't even have to watch to know the outcome.

There would be no Champions League win for Barcelona this season. Pep had been beaten by a solid defensive performance – the same type of performance that Real Madrid had used to defeat them.

After the game, Pep just sat there on the bench, disconsolate. He had tried everything and it had failed. He was tired – exhausted – and completely out of ideas. He needed a break. He needed to come back and try something new.

"I think this is it for me," Pep said, turning to Tito. "I think this might be my last season."

"You're retiring?" Tito asked.

"Not retiring," Pep replied. "Just leaving Barcelona. I need a break, I need to try something fresh. I need something new."

12
REAL AGAIN

May 2014, Allianz Arena, Munich, Germany
Champions League semi-final, Bayern v Real Madrid

"It was always going to be them, wasn't it?" Carles
Planchart sighed as he looked over at Pep.

Pep nodded silently. It had been almost two years
since that fateful Champions League semi-final against
Chelsea. Two years since he'd left Barcelona, walking
away from his boyhood club.

Every day in those two years he'd thought about his

decision to leave. He constantly questioned whether he'd been right to go, but he only had to remember how tired he'd felt during that semi-final, how short of ideas he'd been. He knew it had been the right thing to do.

Tonight felt different. Tonight, he was re-energised and focused.

After Barca, he'd taken a year away from football, and when he'd finally been ready to return he had been flooded with interest and offers. Chelsea, Manchester United – they'd all made inquiries. But there had only been one team for him – the current Champions League holders, Bayern Munich.

His right-hand man Tito Vilanova had taken over the manager's role at Barcelona, but Pep had brought some friendly faces – Domènec Torrent and Carles Planchart – with him to Bayern. He wanted men beside him that he could trust.

The Bayern team didn't need many changes. Pep's focus instead was on how they would play. German football was different to Spanish, based as it was on counter-attacking, high-pressing football rather than the possession-based tactics that most Spanish teams used.

"We can't use the same tactics as I did in Barcelona," Pep told his team of coaches at the start of the season.

There was another reason he wanted to change his style a bit. He had something to prove. Ever since his final season at Barcelona, the rumours had started.

Pep just copied Cruyff's tactics.

He can't win anything without Messi.

He wanted to show that he was capable of creating something different, something unique. He wanted to show that he could win trophies in multiple leagues and countries, and without the presence of Lionel Messi.

"We're still going to be playing total football," Pep told his players. "We've got talented full-backs in Lahm and Alaba," he continued, surveying the team. "If we push them inside to play as holding midfielders, it creates space for Robben and Ribery out wide to use their pace. It allows them to dictate play."

"We can flood the midfield," Carles added. "Dictate the game on our terms, not have it dictated to us."

It was a bold tactic for the Bundesliga, and for the first few months nobody could work out what the team sheet was going to be, based on the line-up. Sometimes there would be as few as two defenders on the team sheet, with several players moving around the pitch and playing in different positions.

It worked magnificently as Bayern made a record-breaking start to the season, advancing several points clear of the rest of the league. They also went deep into the German Cup and made it into the semis of the Champions League.

Tonight's game was the Champions League semi-final and it was against Real Madrid, the team that had stopped Pep from winning the league in his final season at Barca. Although they were no longer managed by Mourinho, Real were still a formidable unit and they'd won the first leg 1-0 in Madrid.

"I think we should go toe-to-toe with them," Philipp Lahm said, leaning into the conversation between Pep and his coaches.

"We can't," Pep replied. He was more than happy to have tactical discussions with his players. He wanted them to be thinking for themselves.

"Why not?" Lahm asked.

"Madrid are powerful, physical, quick," Pep

explained. "Ronaldo, Bale, Modric̀, di María ... you can't match them like that. We need to play *our* way, control the ball and wear them down."

Pep had gone for a more traditional line-up for tonight's game. Kroos and Schweinsteiger were playing at the base of midfield, with Robben, Ribery and Müller behind Mario Mandžukic̀.

"We play our game and we'll get the goals we need, boys," Pep insisted. "We've got so many options going forward, we just have to be patient."

But the game got off to the worst possible start as Sergio Ramos scored two headed goals inside the first 20 minutes. Bayern now trailed 3-0 on aggregate and needed to score four goals to stand a chance of going through.

"Always set pieces. It's the same goal twice over!" Pep cursed, throwing an arm up in the air.

During his early days at Barcelona he'd tried to hide his emotions from his players, in an effort to keep their focus. But he'd quickly discovered that German football was different. The players fed off the energy of the crowd – and the energy of their manager.

Now, 3-0 down, showing his emotions helped Pep generate the energy and motivation that Bayern needed. He had to get his players going – they needed to abandon their patient game plan now and find something new.

Then, with Ribery driving into the box, he was dispossessed and Real Madrid broke quickly, playing the ball through di María and Benzema into Bale before finally Ronaldo finished it off. Real Madrid were now 4-0 up on aggregate.

Pep groaned and stared at the sky. He knew the game was done.

"Counter-attacking is the new style," Carles shrugged, glancing over at Pep.

Pep didn't reply. Counter-attacking might be working here, but it wasn't his style. Real Madrid had won this time, but he was determined to prove that his style was going to win out.

They would play beautiful football *and* they would get results.

13

WORSE THAN TERRIBLE

May 2015, Nou Camp, Barcelona, Spain
Champions League semi-final, Barcelona v Bayern Munich

It was a noise that both Pep and Carles were very familiar with. It was the sound of the Nou Camp stadium in Barcelona. They had ended up back where it had all begun.

"We were bound to be back here eventually," Carles remarked as he walked out alongside Pep.

"I never thought I'd be working out how to stop

Messi," Domènec Torrent chuckled, joining the pair of them in the dugout.

"We can't *stop* Messi," Pep sighed. "We can't stop him, or Xavi or Iniesta."

"How do we win, then?" Carles asked. For the first time in over a year, Pep saw genuine concern on his assistant's face.

It felt strange that this season was almost beginning to feel like a failure. It had only been a couple of weeks since Bayern had clinched their second consecutive Bundesliga title, and here they were, in yet another Champions League semi-final.

"That's why we're doing something unexpected," Pep replied calmly.

"It's risky," Carles said quietly, his face still showing that same concern.

Pep had decided to take that risk. The temptation against a team like Barcelona was to allow them to have the ball and then to sit deep. There was no point going toe-to-toe with them in the midfield – you wouldn't win.

But that was exactly what Pep was going to do. He'd been preparing for this all season, by using three at the back and then flooding the midfield with creative players. And that's what he was doing tonight.

Thiago Alcântara, Philipp Lahm, Xabi Alonso and Bastian Schweinsteiger were all playing. And up front he was relying on the pace and strength of new signing Robert Lewandowski and the technical skill of Thomas Müller.

Pep was still thinking about his game plan when he noticed the Barcelona boss, a former team-mate of his, Luis Enrique, approaching.

"Pep," he said warmly.

"It's been a long time since we were both here," Pep said with a smile as he glanced around the stadium. It was a far cry from the El Clásico days, when every comment from Mourinho had felt like some kind of trap.

"It's been a while since you were here, I'm sure," Luis grinned. "You've been a tough act to follow. I've looked at your team sheet and I still can't work out what formation you're using! Any hints?"

"When you've got players like Messi and Neymar, I don't think it matters too much what formation we use," Pep chuckled.

Those were the two players Pep was worried about. You could dominate the midfield and prevent Barcelona from having possession, but all it took was a single moment from Messi or Neymar and the game would be gone. You couldn't plan for that.

Almost from the whistle, Pep's worst fears were realised. Even with five players around him, Messi was a magnet for the ball, moving easily through the Bayern midfield.

"Every time he gets through, our back three is exposed," Pep groaned, turning to his assistants. Several times Manuel Neuer was forced into making brilliant saves, denying Luis Suárez the opening goal.

"What are our options?" Pep said, looking once more to his assistants, although he already knew the answer.

"I think we've got two options," Carles said. "Either we switch to a four and give ourselves a bit more security, or ... "

"Or?" Pep asked.

"Or we tell them to start fouling Messi," Carles shrugged.

"Let's do the four."

To Pep it felt like a failure to have to change his plans like this. He'd made a mistake and he hated it. It stung even more that he was being undone by the team he'd moulded, the team he'd created.

"We're still well in this," Domènec said, reading Pep's face. "The crowd has got them going. We kill that momentum and then we can start making chances of our own."

Pep hoped that he was right. But he was worried. He was starting to experience what so many managers had felt when they'd played his Barcelona side. There was no way to plan for Lionel Messi.

The change to the four made all the difference. After Barcelona's strong start they had faded and their frustrations were starting to appear. There were just over ten minutes left and it looked as if Bayern were going to hold on for a well-earned 0-0 draw.

"Nil-all is a good result," Domènec said, once more the positive voice in the Bayern camp. "We get Robben and Ribery back, take them back to Munich. There's a win there."

Pep nodded. He knew he was right, but he still felt

that it was a betrayal of his principles. Bayern had frustrated and denied Barcelona, but they were yet to have a shot on target themselves.

Then it happened. The ball was given away cheaply and allowed Messi to run at the Bayern defence, for the first time since the first half.

"No, no, no," Pep whispered, instinctively fearing the worst.

The run was good, the shot was better and it whistled past Neuer and into the near corner. Barcelona had the lead.

0-0 was an OK result, but a 1-0 loss was a terrible one.

But there was worse to come. Pep could even see it coming, but there was nothing he could do. The goal had knocked the heart out of his players – and there were no tactical plans that could prevent that.

Messi added a magnificent second, before Neymar sealed the win. If 1-0 was terrible, there were no words to describe a 3-0 defeat. Bayern were going to be knocked out by a Spanish team in the Champions League semi-finals for the second year running.

And there was nothing Pep could do.

14
OUT ON A HIGH

May 2016, Olympiastadion, Berlin, Germany
DFB-Pokal Final, Borussia Dortmund v Bayern Munich

Three years at Bayern and three Bundesliga titles.

To most managers it would have been the greatest success of their career, but to Pep it felt like a major failure. He may have won yet another title, but for the third year in a row they'd fallen short in the Champions League semi-finals.

A recent defeat to Atlético Madrid finally cemented

a decision that Pep had already made. He'd never intended to stay at Bayern for too long, but early in the season he'd decided that this would be his last.

"Where are we going, then, boss?" Carles had asked him, after he'd told him of his decision to leave.

"You don't have to come with me," Pep reminded him. "We've got a nice thing here. I'm sure Bayern will keep you on."

"You know me and Dom are always going to stick with you," Carles said. "So, where are we going?"

At that time, Pep hadn't known, although he'd had his suspicions. Manchester City, in England, had recently appointed Pep's former Barcelona team-mate Txiki Begiristain as Sporting Director. Txiki hadn't forced the issue, but he'd made it clear that if Pep was ever leaving Bayern, there would be a place for him at City.

At last, Pep made the phone call.

"I think I'm ready," Pep told Txiki one day, "if there's still a place for me."

"Oh yes, absolutely," Txiki replied. "The owners will be delighted to hear you're on board. Are there any players you want us to go after – to try and sign before you join? I don't know if you've had a chance to look over the squad yet?"

Pep *had* done his homework on the Man City squad. They'd won two league titles in the last five years and had players like Sergio Agüero, Kevin De Bruyne and Raheem Sterling. There was quality in there for sure, but there were also areas Pep wanted to change.

"A centre-midfielder," Pep began. "Maybe someone like İlkay Gündoğan at Dortmund."

"Done," Txiki said. "We'll get him."

"Oh. Great," Pep said. He hadn't quite expected them to get the actual player he'd asked for. He'd had plenty of money to work with at Bayern and Barcelona, but it seemed that City were operating on another level altogether. For them, nobody was out of reach.

"And a centre-back," he continued. "Someone who can play out from the back."

"We'll have a look," Txiki replied. Then, after a pause, "It'll be a pleasure to work with you again, Pep."

With his future at City next season now public knowledge, the pressure was on for the rest of the season with Bayern. After a third Bundesliga title had arrived, alongside a third defeat in the Champions League, the final game of the season became the crucial one.

It was the DFB-Pokal final, with Bayern Munich playing their arch-rivals Borussia Dortmund – the only team that had threatened Pep during his time in Germany, and the only team that could prevent him from going out on a high.

He'd stopped using his three at the back system and for the final he reverted to a four at the back, with pace on the wings.

"We keep a high tempo from the first minute, guys," Pep said, looking at each of the players before the match. "This is a cup final, so there are no second chances – we cannot make it up next week."

"No mistakes, boys," Philipp Lahm added.

"We get it into Robert and we support him," Pep continued, gesturing to Robert Lewandowski. "He will hold the ball and we get men around him and that goal will come, I promise, guys, OK?"

The players nodded. They seemed resolute and determined to go out on a high. Pep might be considering his time at Bayern a failure, but to them it had been a great success, and they wanted to give him a good send-off.

The game was tense and, whilst Pep felt Bayern were dominant, they failed to get a goal in either half. Extra time was even more tense and, again, there were no goals. It had been a long season and both sets of players were exhausted.

"I hate penalties," Carles muttered.

Pep agreed. He had no control over penalties. During a game he always felt that he could influence things, but with penalties it was all on the players. There was absolutely nothing he could do but watch.

Both teams missed penalties before it finally came down to Douglas Costa. If he scored, Bayern would win the cup. After a brief wait, he dispatched his penalty coolly and calmly. Bayern had won the cup against their biggest rivals, and Pep was going out on a high.

"Spain first, now Germany," Carles said. "Let's go conquer England."

15
CITY

September 2016, Old Trafford, Manchester, England
Man Utd v Man City

"There's a lot of work that needs to be done here," Pep said, surveying the squad with his team of coaches.

Bayern had been a treble-winning team when Pep had arrived, and there'd been very little he'd needed to change. City were different. Leicester had been the shock winners of the previous season's Premier League, and it had been a couple of years since City had come close.

Pep had brought Domènec and Carles with him to City, but he'd also kept on Brian Kidd, who'd been at City for several years, and brought in former Arsenal midfielder Mikel Arteta. England was a very different country to any he'd managed in before and Pep thought it was necessary to have people around him who understood Premier League football.

"Are you thinking of a lot of transfers?" Mikel asked.

"No, we don't want to make major changes," Pep replied. "The keeper – Joe Hart. How good is he with his feet?"

They all turned to Brian Kidd, the man who knew the City players best.

"He's an excellent shot-stopper," Brian replied, "one of the best." He paused, as if thinking. "His passing's not great, though," he admitted eventually.

"That's the issue," Pep said. "We've got good players, but they're not set up for the way we want to play."

"A centre-back, centre-midfielder and keeper," Carles mused.

"Possibly," Pep shrugged. "De Bruyne, Silva, Sterling, Agüero – those are the key ones. Kompany in defence.

We keep these guys together and that is a winning team."

"Not Yaya Touré?" Mikel asked.

Pep had worked with Yaya at Barcelona before. He knew how good he was, and Yaya had come on leaps and bounds since joining Man City as an attacking midfielder. But he also knew he was a particular type of player. The team would have to be built around him.

"Yaya will play a part," Pep said tactfully. He wasn't quite willing to isolate a club legend. If he was going to move any of them on, it would be gradually.

Over the first few weeks, Pep got to know his players, including the new signings İlkay Gündoğan, John Stones at centre-back and goalkeeper Claudio Bravo.

"Everything starts from the back," he said, addressing the whole team. "The centre-back is the first attacker. If he cannot pass through their forwards, he is no good to me."

He looked at the players, gauging their reactions, to see if there were any who disagreed.

"We may make mistakes," he continued, raising his hands. "I do not mind. Mistakes are good, they help us learn. So have faith in yourselves, you are all good players. Have confidence that you are good enough."

"We are aiming to win everything this season," he said. "That will be our aim for every season. Anything less is not good enough, OK, guys? But also understand that it may not happen straight away – and that's OK too."

The opening games were comfortable for City, but there was one particular date that they all had circled in their diaries: 10th September, away to Man Utd.

Pep had been involved in derbies at both of his previous clubs, so the Manchester derby was nothing new. But there was an extra edge to this game, as the new Manchester United boss was his old friend and foe, José Mourinho.

"It's good to see you again, José," Pep began, smiling warmly at his opposition manager.

"And you too, Pep," José replied. "I hope you've had enough time to put your team together. I know it can take a while for those big money signings to settle."

"I think you've spent your fair share too, José." Pep replied.

José chuckled and walked back to his own technical

area. It wasn't quite as tense as their old El Clásico battles had been, but there was still a degree of tension in the air.

Mourinho was half-right though. Pep's team still wasn't fully settled. Sergio Agüero and Yaya Touré were unavailable, as was Vincent Kompany at centre-back, so Pep was using young striker Kelechi Iheanacho.

"I want you to push up today," he told Kevin De Bruyne before the game. "Effectively form a front two. Keep them on the back foot, high energy, high pressing. They will make a mistake."

City got their opener inside 15 minutes. De Bruyne was sharper than the United defenders and got the ball in front of the centre-back, before racing through and finishing it off. Iheanacho added a second after a De Bruyne shot rebounded off the post 20 minutes later.

Once more, Pep found himself glancing furtively over to José Mourinho's side of the touchline. José was slumped in his seat, a miserable look on his face.

Pep couldn't help but feel a small smile creep onto *his* face. It may have been early days, but he was already starting to enjoy life in Manchester.

16
CHALLENGE

February 2018, Wembley Stadium, London, England
Carabao Cup Final, Arsenal v Man City

" 'Fraudiola'? Really?" Pep said, scrolling down the Twitter feed. He shook his head in mock frustration. "That's not even a pun, is it?"

"I don't know," Carles replied. "It's nonsense though."

"One season without a trophy," Pep continued. "The first time that's ever happened to me. And already they're saying this. Saying I can't win a trophy without Messi. Saying my career is done."

Carles didn't reply. It had been a tough opening season with Man City. There had been good moments – the win at United, plus a few other good wins. But there had been too many defeats, and too many heavy defeats.

They'd been knocked out of the League Cup at the quarter-final stage, the FA Cup in the semis and the Champions League last 16. It was the first time that Pep had failed to reach at least the semis of the Champions League.

And yet Pep was loving it. This felt like his first really big challenge, and he was keen to get working on solutions to the problems. He had a feeling he knew *exactly* how to do it.

"Full-backs and goalkeeper," he said, glancing over the team sheet once again.

"What?" Carles asked.

"Full-backs," Pep said again. "That's the key. If we get high quality full-backs they can stretch the pitch, make it big – and that allows players like Raheem and Kevin to move inside."

"So who are you thinking of?"

Pep had a few players in mind – players who'd caused him problems this season. Kyle Walker of Spurs, Benjamin Mendy of Monaco. He added into that mix Bernardo Silva, Danilo and a new keeper, Ederson.

"This is it," Pep said. "This is the squad."

He'd also moved on a number of players – players he felt were clogging up the squad and were distractions in the dressing room. So now it was streamlined and it was perfect. Every player was pulling in the same direction, every player was with him.

He had his right-back in Walker, but left-back was proving to be an issue. Mendy had picked up an injury and was going to be out for most of the season. But Pep had spotted something else.

"Delph," he said, writing the name of midfielder Fabian Delph in the left-back position.

"What?" Mikel asked. "That can't work, surely?"

"Delph will be defensive, and he's great on the ball," Pep continued. "He moves across and basically makes a back three. That means Walker moves up and we get a two-v-one on that side."

He could see that his coaching team still weren't convinced, but *he* was, and he knew that they'd see it eventually. He knew this was going to work.

With the season getting going, there was just one more tactical switch Pep wanted to make.

"Raheem!" he said, calling over his number seven.

"You've been brilliant, OK. But you can do better," he continued. "I want goals from you, more goals, OK?"

"Sure," Raheem replied.

"The plan is for cut-backs. We overload that right side and then Kevin or Sané or Kyle, they cut it back to the centre of the box, OK?" Pep said.

"Right," Raheem nodded.

"That's your place, OK?" Pep said. "You just wait there and, trust me, you will score so many goals. That's all you need to do. You wait there and the ball will come."

Pep was now confident that the team was ready to go out and win trophies this season. And, after a slow start, the team finally clicked. They won 18 consecutive games in the league, including thrashing both Liverpool and Spurs.

The league title was now within City's grasp, but

their first chance at a trophy came even earlier. They had also made their way to the League Cup final in February. The final was against Arsenal, a team they'd already beaten this season, but Pep knew a final was a different proposition.

"Guys," Pep said. "We've come so far this season and this won't be the last trophy we win. But we want everything. Let's win today and let's get this season really started."

"We know what Arsenal are good at," Pep said. "We know they're going to hold onto the ball, so we disrupt that, we stop them from getting in their flow."

City's opener came from Sergio Agüero, after a mistake by Arsenal in the first half. From then on, it was plain sailing. Kompany and David Silva added second-half goals as City ran out 3-0 winners and Pep sealed his first trophy as Man City boss.

The goals had come from the old guard of Man City, but the team was really playing the Pep way now. He was putting his stamp on this City team.

And they'd barely got started.

17
ONE HUNDRED!

May 2018, St Mary's Stadium, Southampton, England
Southampton v Man City

The League Cup victory had been Pep's first City trophy, but he was keen to ensure it wasn't his last. There had been disappointments in the FA Cup and the Champions League, but the Premier League was still firmly within City's grasp.

They sealed the league title in April, after Man Utd failed to beat West Brom. Once again, Pep had beaten his arch-rival José Mourinho. The title may have been sealed, but Pep was still working his team as hard as ever.

"Do you remember in La Liga?" Carles asked him after one training session.

"Which season?" Pep asked.

"The last one," Carles said. "José's Real Madrid got to a hundred points and took our record."

"Yeah." Pep hesitated, not sure where this was going. He wasn't too keen on reliving those memories.

"Well, I've been thinking," Carles continued. "It's José who has the points record here with Chelsea – they got 95 points quite a few years ago. If we keep going this season, we could take that record from him. Wouldn't that be sweet?"

Pep shook his head, laughing.

"I'm not in this to try and take records from people," he said. "It's not personal. We just want to win."

"OK, OK," Carles said. "But we still want 100 points, right?"

He was right. If City could become the first Premier League team to get 100 points in a season, it would be a real vindication of Pep's methods and his style of football. Pep was also disappointed at how poorly they'd done in the Champions League, and sealing the title with a record points tally would go some way towards making up for that.

The players were fully on board and in fact seemed more focused than they had been when the title was on the line.

It all came down to the final day of the season, with City away at Southampton. They were already on 97 points, so needed the win to take them to the magical 100 points they were after.

"We all know what we want today, guys," Pep said. "A win. Nothing else is OK for us. We want that 100 points. I know I do, and I know all of you do. So let's fight for it."

Southampton were also keen to end the season on a high in front of their own fans. For long periods of the game they dominated the ball, and Claudio Bravo was forced into a number of good saves.

"What's happening, guys?" Pep said, turning to his coaching team.

"We need more attacking players on," Mikel replied.

With the absence of Agüero and with Gabriel Jesus only half-fit, Pep was using Raheem Sterling as a striker. But on the hour mark, he made the change.

"Gabi!" he called, getting his striker over to him.

"I know you're not fully fit," he said, putting his arm round him, "but just work as hard as you can. Just be aware. It might be immediately, it might be in the last minute, but be ready for that chance. It will come."

He took off his left-back Fabian Delph for Jesus, switching to an attacking three at the back, effectively playing Leroy Sané as a wing-back.

"If that doesn't do the trick, I don't know what will," Pep laughed.

It was rare for Pep to go on the offensive so early, but this was effectively a cup final. They just wanted the win – they *needed* the win.

For the next 30 minutes it didn't work and, as the board ticked over into the 90th minute, Pep could only hold his head in his hands.

"We've won the title. So why does it feel like we're failing?" Pep groaned, turning to his assistants.

"Wait! Wait!" Carles shouted and Mikel joined him,

jumping to his feet. Pep turned and saw the ball floating over the top, towards Gabriel Jesus in the Southampton box.

"Go on, Gabi!" he said, feeling his muscles tighten as if he was kicking the ball himself.

Jesus was calm – far calmer than Pep felt. He coolly lifted the ball over the keeper and into the back of the net.

Instantly Pep sprinted along the touchline, jumping high into the air as his coaching staff and subs streamed past him, joining in the celebrations.

"Come on!" Pep roared, staring up to the sky.

It was rare that he celebrated so passionately, but after everything he had done in his career, this felt sweet. A hundred points – the most ever in a Premier League season. This felt like one of his greatest moments.

Pep's football was dominating England.

18
"THAT'S THE WIN!"

January 2019, Etihad Stadium, Manchester, England
Man City v Liverpool

"Seven points is a big gap at this stage," Pep mused.

The successes of last season were still fresh in the minds of the players and the fans, but Pep had already moved on. City may have sealed the title with a record points total, but the defeats in the Champions League had shown him that there was a long way to go with this team.

Klopp's Liverpool had strengthened over the summer and they had started the season in sublime form, barely dropping a point. City were struggling to keep up at times.

"Every time we win, they win as well," Mikel moaned. "And every time we lose, they still win."

"We've been here before," Carles replied. "Real Madrid under José – they matched us every step of the way. This isn't unknown."

"And we lost the title that year," Pep reminded him. "We made mistakes, we got over-confident."

Carles didn't reply. Tensions were running high in the dressing room and Pep was keen to ensure that the players and the fans didn't get wind of it. He had to take all the pressure on himself, not allowing any of it to affect the players.

They had missed Kevin De Bruyne for most of the season, but the word was that he was back fit for tonight's game against Liverpool.

"I can't play, boss," Kevin told him. "I won't be able to play at all."

"*You* know that," Pep replied. "And *I* know that. But

they don't know that. Just the fact that you're in the squad is going to give us an edge."

Liverpool were the team that had knocked City out of the Champions League, and Pep was keen to use any tricks he had to his advantage.

"This game is like a cup final, guys," Pep told his team. "We lose this and the title is gone, OK, guys? We can forget it. But if we win, then we close the gap and the momentum is ours. Then they are the ones who panic. OK, guys?"

Before the players went out, Pep called his captain, Vincent Kompany, over.

"Don't let them lose their heads, OK, Vinnie?" he said. "But also keep that intensity – let's go toe-to-toe with them. Use the crowd."

Kompany nodded. He was up for this – the whole team was. They knew the importance of this game.

The game started at a frenetic pace. Both teams seemed to have forgotten the way they usually played football and were sucked in by the atmosphere. Tactics went out of the window, replaced by hard running and flying tackles.

Pep was OK with that, even after John Stones was forced into a dramatic goal-line clearance. The higher the intensity, the better it would be for City.

"Lovren's the weak link for them," Domènec said, coming forward to share his thoughts. "And get Sergio as far away from Van Dijk as possible."

"Yeah, agreed," Pep said.

The goal came moments later.

Agüero nipped in front of Lovren, controlled the ball and blasted it into the top corner from a tight angle, in the way that only he could.

Pep's face remained blank, giving nothing away. This was the goal they needed, but there was still a long way to go. As confident as he was in his team, Pep couldn't see them stopping Liverpool from scoring for the whole 90 minutes. They would need a second.

In the second half, Liverpool struck back through Roberto Firmino.

Almost immediately, they made a sub, taking off Sadio Mané for Shaqiri.

"They want the draw," Mikel said.

"They're going to sit back," Pep replied. "This is when

we push on and go for it. Almost like we did against Southampton last year."

The team got the message and began to push forward, forcing Liverpool onto the back foot.

Sterling took the ball and slid it into Leroy Sané. His touch was perfect and he drilled it across the keeper and into the far corner, off the post.

"Come on!" Pep roared, now showing his emotions, turning to the crowd and pumping them up. He wanted them to show their support for his team.

"That's it! That's the win! That's the title back in our hands!" he bellowed, grabbing Mikel Arteta.

It didn't matter that City were still four points behind. Now Pep could sense it. They were in this race just as much as Liverpool.

19
CRACKED IT

February 2020, Bernabéu Stadium, Madrid, Spain
Real Madrid v Man City

"This year," Pep said, "It's Champions League or nothing. That's the one we want."

The win against Liverpool last year had changed the momentum. Liverpool had stuttered after that game, but City had marched on, going on a massive unbeaten run and winning an unprecedented domestic treble – the Premier League, the FA Cup and the League Cup.

It was one of his best achievements as a manager, but Pep still wasn't satisfied. City had once again fallen short in the Champions League, losing to Tottenham at the quarter-final stage in an incredibly dramatic game.

He'd been stung by accusations that he had tinkered too much with his tactics and cost his team in the Champions League. In fact, Pep felt it had been the opposite.

"The Champions League is different," he said, looking back over City's previous results. They'd conceded huge numbers of goals to Monaco, Liverpool and Tottenham.

"We can't play the way we normally do, can we?" Carles pondered. "We need to be a bit tighter."

"It's effectively a two-legged cup final," Pep replied. "We need to make sure we stay in the tie from the first leg. Too often we've already put ourselves out of it."

Pep felt that his team had already gone as far as they could in the Premier League and in England. They'd won it all and, although he was still desperate to do it all again, the Champions League was the trophy he really wanted.

Attempting to balance the multiple competitions was proving tricky, but shortly after the start of the season the decision was made for Pep. Liverpool had started the season with several consecutive wins, whilst City had started slowly.

"The title's gone," Pep conceded. It stung a little bit, but he knew that his team would be back. Now the Champions League was 100% their priority.

The last 16 set them up with one of the harder ties in the competition, against Real Madrid. The first leg was in the Santiago Bernabéu, packed with thousands of Real Madrid fans who wanted nothing more than to see Pep beaten again.

"What's the team, then?" Carles asked.

Pep rubbed his hands across his head. There was a part of him that wanted to go with his usual team, to try to dominate the game from the start with their possession style. But it had failed him for the last three years and he knew it was time for something different.

"4-4-2," he murmured. "Kevin and Bernardo as the front two, hard-working and putting pressure on their centre-backs. Gabi at left wing."

"And in the middle?" Carles asked.

"Gundo and Rodri," Pep replied. "Control the middle, stop them from playing their passes. We have Riyad on the other side who's capable of magic. We close the game out and then push for a winner in the second half."

"It's risky," Carles muttered.

"It's the *opposite* of risky," Pep replied. "It's so much safer. It's something we've not done before."

The team were on board. They were a group of players who believed in everything that Pep had said and were willing to go after it.

The tactic worked perfectly for the first half, even when Aymeric Laporte went off injured. City controlled the space rather than the ball, limiting Real Madrid to shots from long distance. And they even had a number of chances themselves, Mahrez and Jesus both going close.

"This is going exactly as we wanted," Pep said. "We just need that goal."

For the first time in his career, he was almost considering accepting the 0-0 draw. There had been so many times they'd lost the tie in the first leg. He wasn't going to let that happen again.

"Don't change anything, lads," Pep told his team at half-time. "We will get the goal we need."

Even when Real Madrid scored the opening goal, he still felt confident that City were going to get this.

But with 15 minutes to go, he made his first sub – Raheem Sterling for Bernardo Silva.

"Raheem, use your pace," he told him. "Get in behind, make them challenge you. Kevin will find your runs, just trust him."

It was the first sign that he was going to go for it. He could sense that it was the right moment. Madrid had been working harder than City all night and they were starting to tire.

It was time to strike.

A few minutes later, City got their equaliser. De Bruyne wriggled his way into the box, before crossing for Jesus to head home.

Barely five minutes later, City took the lead. Sterling burst into the box, before being taken out by Carvajal. The resulting penalty was tucked away by De Bruyne.

In the space of five minutes City had turned the tie on its head.

"I told you," Pep said, grabbing Carles. "I told you that would work. This is what we've been working for. The Champions League."

"We've got a long way to go," Carles replied, trying to lower expectations.

"I know, but I think we've got it cracked," Pep said, smiling. "I think we've finally cracked it."

20
THE PEP WAY

May 2021, Etihad Stadium, Manchester, England
Champions League semi-final, Man City v PSG

"Why is it snowing in May?" Pep moaned, looking out over the Etihad Stadium pitch, where there was still light snow covering the pitch. "Sometimes I hate this country."

Behind him Carles chuckled, but once more there was a nervous energy in the air. A lot had changed in the last year. The coronavirus pandemic had brought the footballing world to a halt, and when it had finally returned it had returned without the fans.

City had once again exited the Champions League, this time in the quarter-finals, despite their success against Real Madrid.

They had lost the league title to Liverpool, finishing the season with just a League Cup trophy to their name.

Pep had thought they'd cracked the Champions League, and in fact he still believed they had. He was still confident – and now he felt he was right to be.

Tonight he was in his first Champions League semi-final as Manchester City's manager. He was on the verge of leading Man City to their first ever Champions League final – and his first since 2011.

For Pep, this was still everything that he'd been working towards.

"We've already got the League Cup," he began, looking at his team. "The Premier League is in our hands. But this is the one we've been working for. This is the trophy we've wanted for five years, OK guys?"

The team murmured in agreement. They knew exactly what he'd been after, what they had all been after. They'd won everything in England – this trophy was the only thing that had evaded them.

"I know we've got a good lead from the first leg," Pep continued, reminding them of the 2-1 win they'd had in Paris. "But that's gone now. This is the second leg," he added. "We know that they're capable. Neymar, Mbappé, di María – they will be capable of producing moments of magic. But so are we, OK guys? We keep focused, we do what we did in the first leg and we win this."

The players nodded. Pep had reminded them to stay focused, but he hadn't needed to. They knew exactly what they needed to do. They were even more focused than he was.

"Boss, I've got news," Carles said, approaching him as they left the dressing room.

"What is it?" Pep asked.

"Mbappé," Carles said. "He's out."

"I thought he was on the bench," Pep replied.

"That's a ploy," Carles said. "He won't been playing at all is what I'm hearing."

Pep nodded. He'd been there and had done the same

thing. Even without Mbappé, PSG were still dangerous opposition and City had slipped up in the Champions League before.

There was still snow on the pitch and, even though it was May, there was a real chill in the air.

"It's a shame there are no fans," Pep murmured, glancing round the empty stadium.

He had been in Manchester for so long now, he would have loved to have shared this moment with the City fans. He knew they were going to reach the final. He was confident.

City stuck with the same 4-4-2 that had worked so successfully against Real Madrid last season. De Bruyne and Bernardo Silva were operating as the front two, with Foden and Mahrez giving creativity on the wings.

They struck inside 10 minutes. De Bruyne's shot was parried by the PSG keeper and Mahrez fired in the rebound. Pep didn't react, simply turning and marching back to his seat, slumping into it besides Carles.

"I think we're going to do it," Carles said.

Pep didn't reply.

Even when Mahrez scored again in the second half

to put City 2-0 up, Pep only allowed himself a subtle pump of the fist.

It was only at full time that it really hit him.

He had been to Champions League finals before, but not like this. At Barcelona it had been so easy, and even at Bayern it had been relatively easy.

But this was something different. He'd had to fight for this, he'd had to change his tactics and adapt.

Even when it seemed that things had got away from him, he'd changed his tactics and got it back. He had done it his way, not Cruyff's way, not José's way, not Klopp's way.

It had been Pep's way that had got him to this Champions League final, that had got him this far.

It had been Pep's way that had won the Premier League three times. He had now been at City longer than he had been at any other club. He didn't know what the future held for him, whether it was at City or if it was going to be somewhere else.

But he knew that, wherever he was going to end up, his team would always play football the Pep way.

HOW MANY
HAVE YOU READ?